Time Management Workbook for Students

Dr. Emily Schwartz

For Avery Rose

CONTENTS

Each section contains 10 exercises designed to help students improve their time management skills through organization, focus, and motivation.

ACKNOWLEDGMENTS

This book is a product of all I've learned from every student I've ever taught and every teacher I've ever had. Thank you for helping me be a life long learner, challenging me to see new perspectives, and motivating me to never stop trying new things.

INTRODUCTION

Time management is one of the most crucial skills necessary for success in school. It's not enough to just be "smart." Students must also have the discipline, organization, and time management skills to finish their work efficiently with maximum retention and minimal stress. These skills don't develop by acquiring information, they develop by forming habits over an extended period of time. In other words, someone can't just tell you how to have good time management skills. You have to apply that information and practice it for habits to stick. That's what this book helps students accomplish.

This book is divided into three parts. In Part 1, you'll learn how to get organized. Organization is the foundation of any good time management plan and you'll learn how to keep track of your important deadlines in a way that makes sense. Once you get organized, it's time to get focused. Part 2 centers on avoiding distractions so you can do the work you planned to do as efficiently as possible. Finally, in Part 3, you'll learn to combat stress, particularly in the busiest times of your semester so you can continue to apply your time management knowledge effectively.

What makes this book different from other time management workbooks is its use of The Time Diet method. Most students are told to "do the most important thing first" which can be overwhelming. What if everything I have to do is important? The Time Diet offers a more "digestible" approach that is easy to apply and helps students create balance in their lives. In The Time Diet, everything you do belongs to one of three Food

Groups. Your Meats are your difficult tasks that require a lot of thinking. Your Vegetables are easier tasks that are still important, but don't require the same amount of cognitive power. Your Desserts are the fun things in your life: your hobbies, your social time, anything you look forward to.

The trick to having great time management skills and a low stress level is to tackle a "balanced diet" of tasks each day. Ideally, you'll do some difficult things, some easier things, and some fun things. Unfortunately, we don't naturally work like this, but with a little work and training, it will come easily.

As you move through this workbook, remember that all students work a little bit differently. The point of this book is not to tell you exactly what to do. The point is to give you a rough guideline and show you how to figure out what works best for you.

Why did I write this book? I put this workbook together because I've been there. I've taught K-12 students, undergraduate students, masters students, and college graduates. I've also been a college student three times (bachelors, masters, and Ph.D.) Through all those experiences, I've fought through some serious time management battles, and helped my students get through their own difficulties as well. This book is a culmination of everything I wish my students had known and everything I wish I had known before embarking on my academic career.

This workbook is an outgrowth of the book "The Time Diet: Time Management for College Survival" and The Time Diet blog. Check out www.TheTimeDiet.org for more details, or search for the book on Amazon.com.

Good luck on your time management journey.

PART 1

LET'S GET ORGANIZED

Are you an organized person? If you're not, don't worry. It's not as difficult as you may think. Organization is all about planning ahead and documenting that plan in a way that is easy to access and remember. Planning your time in advance and keeping track of your deadlines are two crucial skills required for good time management. If your deadlines aren't organized in a way that is easy to reference, you'll be likely to procrastinate and forget something is due.

Different organizational strategies will work better for different students. The point of this section is to help teach you basic principles of organization so you can apply them in whichever manner works best for you. Some students are extremely neat and have no problem keeping track of a meticulously organized filing system for all their papers. Other students struggle with that level of organization and need a simple way to plan for the week ahead. No matter which type of student you are, it's possible to organize your time in a way that enables you to plan ahead and meet your deadlines.

In this section, you'll find ten worksheets designed to teach you how to choose a list and a calendar, categorize your tasks, use start dates, apply the Five Minute Rule, and more. When you finish the ten worksheets, you'll be armed with the skills to organize your semester in a way that ensures you protect time to do all the things that important to you, while keeping your stress level as low as possible.

Finally, don't forget to let go of your past habits while doing these exercises. Just because you've always done something one way, doesn't mean you can't be open to new suggestions. Part of being a good student is always being open to new strategies that can improve your academic achievement.

#1: Your Time Management Attitude

Time management: Teachers always talk about it, but what does it mean? In the space below, write a few words, phrases, or feelings that you associate with time management.

Reflection Questions

1. Look at the words you wrote above. Are they negative, positive, or neutral words?

2. What are some of the benefits of time management?

3. Why do you think some people have a negative view of time management when the benefits are so positive?

#2: Time Management Food Groups

"Time management is easy, just do the most important thing first!" Have you heard that advice before? What happens when everything is important? The thing to remember about juggling responsibilities is that when *everything* is a priority, *nothing* is a priority. That's why in The Time Diet, we categorize before we prioritize. Everything you do during the day belongs to one of three Food Groups.

1. **Meats**: Difficult tasks that require a lot of focus and concentration
2. **Vegetables**: Easier tasks that, while still important, don't require a lot of thought
3. **Desserts**: Enjoyable tasks or activities

Think about some of the tasks you do frequently during the school year. Use the template below to write some sample Meat, Vegetable, and Dessert tasks from your life.

My Time Management Food Groups

Meats *(difficult things)*	
Vegetables *(easier things)*	
Desserts *(fun things)*	

Reflection Questions

1. Review the tasks you listed in your Food Groups chart. Which task do you look forward to the most? Which Food Group does it belong to?

2. Why do you look forward to it?

3. Which task do you look forward to the least? Which Food Group does it belong to?

4. Why do you dislike it?

5. Remember, the key to great time management is to do a "balanced diet" of tasks each day: a few difficult things, a few easy things, and a few enjoyable things. Why might it be difficult to do that?

6. What can happen if you try to do too many Meat tasks in one day?

7. What can happen if you try to do too many Dessert tasks in one day?

#3: Planning Your Balanced Day

A balanced day of Meats, Vegetables, and Desserts doesn't just...happen. You need to plan your day, week, and month in advance so you don't let Meat tasks pile up. Let's practice!

For the next 5 days, keep a to-do list on the following pages. Follow these steps:

1. Write down all of your Meats, Vegetables, and Desserts.
2. Each day, pick one task from each category that you are going to prioritize. We will call those "focus tasks."
3. When will you complete your focus tasks? Assign a time to each one
4. As you move through the day, complete your focus tasks at the assigned time. In between those tasks, fill in other tasks from your list.

Now you've created a balanced outline for your day. You've thought about your priorities in advance so they don't catch you by surprise.

For Example

Meat tasks Study for History Start English paper Start Math project	**Focus Task** Start English paper **Time:** 3:30pm
Vegetable tasks Clean desk Write Thank You to Grandma Finish Science worksheet	**Focus Task** Write Thank You **Time:** 7:00pm
Dessert tasks Call Amy Practice soccer Watch TV	**Focus Task** Call Amy **Time:** 8:30pm

Day #1

Meat tasks	Focus Task Time:
Vegetable tasks	Focus Task Time:
Dessert tasks	Focus Task Time:

Day #2

Meat tasks	Focus Task
	Time:
Vegetable tasks	**Focus Task**
	Time:
Dessert tasks	**Focus Task**
	Time:

Day #3

Meat tasks	Focus Task Time:
Vegetable tasks	Focus Task Time:
Dessert tasks	Focus Task Time:

Day #4

Meat tasks	Focus Task Time:
Vegetable tasks	Focus Task Time:
Dessert tasks	Focus Task Time:

Day #5

Meat tasks	Focus Task
	Time:
Vegetable tasks	Focus Task
	Time:
Dessert tasks	Focus Task
	Time:

#4 Using Start Dates

When your teacher assigns homework, your first question is likely, "When is it due?"
To be a good time manager, you should not only be concerned with due dates, but also the equally important start date.

Due Date: When an assignment needs to be finished

Start Date: When *you* plan to begin it

Start dates help us avoid procrastination and they need a place in your calendar. Review the excerpt from a sample syllabus shown below. Six assignments have been chosen for you.

1. Write the due dates of these assignments in your calendar on the following page
2. Assign a start date for each task
3. Write that start date in your calendar

An example has already been done for you:

```
                    Time Management 101

    Unit 1

        Time management worksheet          Due Sept. 8th

        Read Chapter 1- 20 pages           Due Sept. 17th

        "My Time Killers" essay- 2 pages   Due Sept. 17th

        Read Chapter 2- 22 pages           Due Sept. 24th

        Class blog reflection 3-4 paragraphs   Due Sept. 29th

        Test on Chapters 1 and 2           Due October 8th
```

September

S	M	T	W	TH	F	S
		1	2	3 Start TM Worksheet	4	5
6	7	8 TM Worksheet Due	9	10	11	12
13	14	15	16	17	18	19
20	21	22	23	24	25	26
27	28	29	30			

October

S	M	T	W	TH	F	S
				1	2	3
4	5	6	7	8	9	

#5 Creating a Study Schedule

Studying is a difficult Meat task, so you have to break it up into smaller pieces. Pretend you have 2 weeks to study for a history test that covers 3 chapters of reading. In the box below, you'll see a few sample strategies people use to study. In the calendar below, write out a study schedule. You don't have to use all the strategies, you can use each strategy as many times as you'd like, or you can make up your own! Just pick a schedule that would work for you and break up the studying over several days. Be sure to include how many hours you'll study each day and if you'll take any days off.

For example, on Sunday, you might write "study flashcards, 1 hour."

Reread text	Make flashcards	Study flashcards	Complete sample questions
Study in a group	Meet with professor	Outline chapter	

S	M	T	W	TH	F	S
					Test Day!	

Study Schedule Reflection Questions

1. How many hours total did you plan to study?

2. Explain why you chose the strategies you used

3. Look at the schedule you created. Can you think of some things that might come up during the week that would force you to change your schedule? What might those things be?

#6 Choosing a Calendar

Choosing the right calendar is important. Some people use a digital calendar, either on their computers, phones, or other device. Others prefer a paper calendar on their desks or in their bags. Which do you prefer? Your job is to research three digital calendars and three paper calendars to decide which features you like. You can do your research either online or in an office supply store.

Digital Calendars

1. Name of application: Brief description of features: What do you like about it?   What do you dislike about it?   Would you use it? Why or why not?

2. Name of application: Brief description of features: What do you like about it?   What do you dislike about it?   Would you use it? Why or why not?

3. Name of application:

Brief description of features:

What do you like about it?

What do you dislike about it?

Would you use it? Why or why not?

Paper Calendars

1. Brand:

Description: (Weekly? Monthly? Big? Small?)

What do you like about it?

What do you dislike about it?

Would you use it? Why or why not?

2. Brand:

Description: (Weekly? Monthly? Big? Small?)

What do you like about it?

What do you dislike about it?

Would you use it? Why or why not?

3. Brand:

Description: (Weekly? Monthly? Big? Small?)

What do you like about it?

What do you dislike about it?

Would you use it? Why or why not?

#7 More Than Academics

Homework, tests, and other academic deadlines likely take up a lot of space on your calendar, but what other types of deadlines belong there? Think through some other obligations in your life that are important to remember. What other types of events and deadlines belong on your calendar? They might be social, hobbies, extracurricular activities, scholarship deadlines, family commitments, etc. List 10 of these deadlines below and why they are important to add to your calendar.

Other Types of Deadlines

1.   Type of Deadline:

      Why is it important to remember?

2.   Type of Deadline:

      Why is it important to remember?

3.   Type of Deadline:

      Why is it important to remember?

4.   Type of Deadline:

      Why is it important to remember?

5.   Type of Deadline:

Why is it important to remember?

6.   Type of Deadline:

Why is it important to remember?

7.   Type of Deadline:

Why is it important to remember?

8.   Type of Deadline:

Why is it important to remember?

9.   Type of Deadline:

Why is it important to remember?

10.   Type of Deadline:

Why is it important to remember?

#8 The Five Minute Rule

When looking at your list, you'll quickly find things that seem to stay on the list forever that you never want to finish! They are usually quick, Vegetable tasks that you put off forever.

Take the Five Minute Challenge!

Set a timer for 5 minutes and do something, ANYTHING productive until the timer goes off. You can clean something, start a homework assignment, call your family, anything you want.

Are you finished? Great! Now answer the following questions:

1. What did you do for the 5 minutes?

2. Did the 5 minutes seem longer or shorter than you expected?

3. Did you accomplish more or fewer things during that time than expected?

4. What are a few short, easy tasks that you put off frequently? Why do you put them off?

5. Could you use the Five Minute Rule to help cross them of your list?

#9 Time Management Karma

The Golden Rule of time management is:

"Treat other people's time the way you'd like yours to be treated"

Think of a situation where someone wasted your time.
Describe what happened and how you felt about it

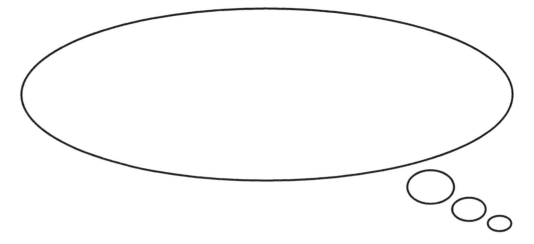

Now think of a situation where YOU wasted someone's time.
Describe what happened and how you felt about it

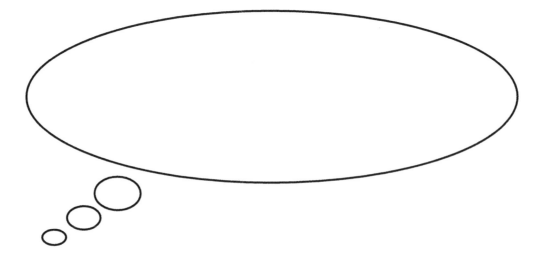

Reflection Questions

1. Compare the two situations you described on the previous page. How are they similar? How are they different?

2. What steps can you take to improve your "Time Management Karma" and make sure you are conscious of whether or not you're wasting other people's time?

#10 Organization Scavenger Hunt

Keeping your deadlines organized isn't difficult and just requires a simple plan and consistency...BUT it's definitely easier if other aspects of your life are organized as well.

Go on an Organization Scavenger Hunt in your life. Look in these three places, describe what you see, and then rate your organization on a scale of 1-10.

---

1. Backpack

What do you see?

Organization on a scale of 1-10?:

---

2. Closet

What do you see?

Organization on a scale of 1-10?:

---

3. Desk

What do you see?

Organization on a scale of 1-10?:

Reflection Questions

1. Are your deadlines and calendar MORE organized or LESS organized than your backpack, closet, and desk? Why do you think that is?

2. What small changes could you make to your routine that would improve your organization as a whole?

PART 2
LET'S GET FOCUSED

Now that you've worked on your organization, it's time to work on your focus. The two go hand in hand. Once you've set aside time to work, you'll want to finish that work as efficiently as possible so everything you planned fits in your schedule.

Unfortunately, students have many distractions competing for their focus. When you sit down to work, you may be tempted to check your email, chat with a friend, watch your favorite show, or even just space out. Distracted work helps us define the difference between busy and productive.

If you sit at your desk for 4 hours with your class notes in front of you, you may think you're studying for a test, but if you're distracted and not really processing the information, you've been busy, but not productive. Busy means you've filled time. Productive means you've pushed through your distractions to accomplish something meaningful in a focused manner.

This section will help you identify your unique distractions and help you discover strategies to eliminate them while you're working. You'll learn how to strategically pick the right time of day for your work, identify and remove Time Killers, annotate your reading effectively, avoid procrastination, pick the best study location, and more. If you find that you're struggling to focus on your work, you're not alone. Many students find it's difficult to get "in the zone" while working.

Remember, that each student is susceptible to different distractions and focus is a habit that takes lots of patience and repetition to form. Don't be discouraged!.

#1 Time Buckets

Are you a night owl or a morning person? To work most efficiently, it's best to prioritize your difficult Meat tasks when you're most focused rather than using that prime focus time for easier Vegetable tasks.

Think of your day as being broken up into "Time Buckets." Assign a number 1-5 to each time bucket based on how much energy and focus you have during the given time period. 1 means you have no energy and 5 means you have a ton. (If you're usually sleeping, put a 1)

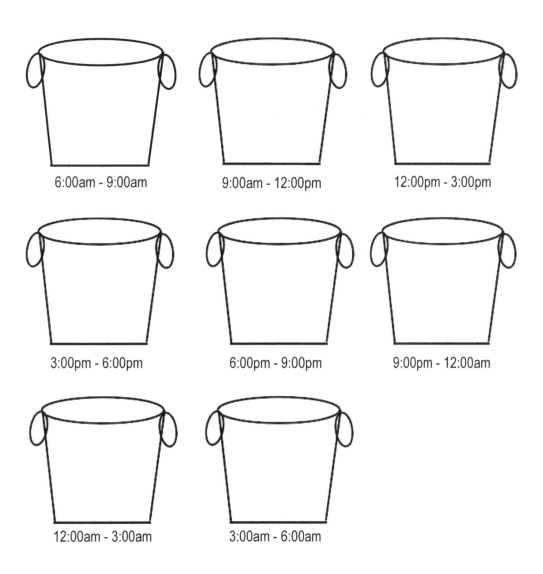

6:00am - 9:00am   9:00am - 12:00pm   12:00pm - 3:00pm

3:00pm - 6:00pm   6:00pm - 9:00pm   9:00pm - 12:00am

12:00am - 3:00am   3:00am - 6:00am

Reflection Questions

1. Based on your focus and energy levels, which Time Buckets should contain your Meat tasks?

2. Which Time Buckets should contain your Vegetable tasks?

3. Do you currently structure your day that way? Why or why not?

4. Are you a night owl or a morning person?

5. Do you think that has a positive, neutral, or negative effect on your time management?

#2 Time Killers

Time Killers are little things that waste our time without our permission. For the next 5 days, keep track of all the things that distract you. Remember, things like email, your phone, snacking, and chatting with friends are not necessarily bad, but they become Time Killers when they distract you without your permission.

Day 1

1. Time Killer that distracted you:

    What did it distract you from?

    How long did it distract you?

2. Time Killer that distracted you:

    What did it distract you from?

    How long did it distract you?

3. Time Killer that distracted you:

    What did it distract you from?

    How long did it distract you?

4. Time Killer that distracted you:

    What did it distract you from?

    How long did it distract you?

Day 2

1. Time Killer that distracted you:

   What did it distract you from?

   How long did it distract you?

2. Time Killer that distracted you:

   What did it distract you from?

   How long did it distract you?

3. Time Killer that distracted you:

   What did it distract you from?

   How long did it distract you?

4. Time Killer that distracted you:

   What did it distract you from?

   How long did it distract you?

5. Time Killer that distracted you:

   What did it distract you from?

   How long did it distract you?

Day 3

1. Time Killer that distracted you:

   What did it distract you from?

   How long did it distract you?

2. Time Killer that distracted you:

   What did it distract you from?

   How long did it distract you?

3. Time Killer that distracted you:

   What did it distract you from?

   How long did it distract you?

4. Time Killer that distracted you:

   What did it distract you from?

   How long did it distract you?

5. Time Killer that distracted you:

   What did it distract you from?

   How long did it distract you?

Day 4

1. Time Killer that distracted you:

    What did it distract you from?

    How long did it distract you?

2. Time Killer that distracted you:

    What did it distract you from?

    How long did it distract you?

3. Time Killer that distracted you:

    What did it distract you from?

    How long did it distract you?

4. Time Killer that distracted you:

    What did it distract you from?

    How long did it distract you?

5. Time Killer that distracted you:

    What did it distract you from?

    How long did it distract you?

Day 5

1.   Time Killer that distracted you:

    What did it distract you from?

    How long did it distract you?

2.   Time Killer that distracted you:

    What did it distract you from?

    How long did it distract you?

3.   Time Killer that distracted you:

    What did it distract you from?

    How long did it distract you?

4.   Time Killer that distracted you:

    What did it distract you from?

    How long did it distract you?

5.   Time Killer that distracted you:

    What did it distract you from?

    How long did it distract you?

Reflection Questions

Look back over your Time Killer journal for the past 5 days:

1. What were your three most common distractions?

2. What were you doing when you became distracted? Was it easier to stay focused on some tasks more than others?

3. What can you do to remove those top distractions before you start working?

#3 Focus on Reading

Reading is an important skill in college. It's helpful to be able to read quickly, but it's *more* important to be able to *comprehend* quickly. Many students find it's easier to comprehend text when they annotate as they read. Annotating also makes studying easier by quickly reminding you which parts of the text were important.

Take out a pen and read the following segment of text as though you're studying for a test on the material. Find a way to mark any main points or important things you'll want to come back to later. If you're tempted to use a highlighter for this task instead of a pen, remember: we tend to go "highlighter happy" and highlight everything when we're using this tool. With a pen, it's easier to mark *why* you felt something was important so you can remember later.

Do you have your pen? Ready, Go! ───────────────────────────

Chapter 1: Effective Email Communication

Email is a common form of communication in the workplace, so understanding how to write emails effectively is important. There are three main ways to improve email communication: maximize the subject line, don't abuse the Reply All button, and keep the message brief. The subject line should be used as a summary of what the email is about. It helps the reader prepare for what you'll talk about and allows him or her to assess at a glance if it is something he or she is able to tackle right now. When you leave the subject line blank, or use a vague title, your reader doesn't know what your communication will be about which means his or her understanding of your main message could be impaired. The Reply All button is meant to easily keep all parties of a message on the same page, but just because the original email was sent to multiple people, that doesn't mean they all need to see your reply. If your reply doesn't apply to all people on the email, then only send your response to the sender. Otherwise, you'll clog people's email inboxes with unnecessary messages which distract from your communications that actually are important. Finally, and most importantly, when you do send a message, keep it brief. People get a ton of email and they may only give yours a brief glance. Make sure your main point and the desired action you wish your reader to take are very clear. Email inboxes receive a lot of clutter, but by following these three simple strategies, you can help make your messages stand out.

Reflection Questions

1. What parts of the text did you annotate? Why?

2. Were there any parts of the text that you didn't feel were terribly important? Why?

3. Where can you go to read and easily stay focused? Why?

4. Where can you read and find it's hard to stay focused? Why?

#4 Change of Scenery

Where do you do your homework? The location you choose to work has a lot to do with how much you're able to focus. Some people need background noise in order to focus. Others need silence. Some people are distracted if they work near the kitchen. Others are distracted if they work near their bed.

Experiment with three different work locations and record what you like or dislike about them. Ideas include a library, your desk, a chair outside, a coffee shop, etc...

Place #1

Location:

Have you worked there before?

What do you like about it?

What do you dislike about it?

Are you able to focus here?

Place #2

Location:

Have you worked there before?

What do you like about it?

What do you dislike about it?

Are you able to focus here?

Place #3

Location:

Have you worked there before?

What do you like about it?

What do you dislike about it?

Are you able to focus here?

#5 Procrastination

Procrastination is the enemy of time management. We procrastinate when we don't want to do something. The problem with procrastination is that it doesn't *always* end badly. Sometimes, we wait until the last minute, and everything turns out fine! Then, we're more likely to keep procrastinating until it *doesn't* turn out "fine." When you're tempted to procrastinate, it's important to remember the times when procrastination didn't work out.

Think of three times you've procrastinated and wish you hadn't.

Procrastination Situation #1

Why did you procrastinate and what happened?

What do you wish you'd done instead?

Procrastination Situation #2

Why did you procrastinate and what happened?

What do you wish you'd done instead?

Procrastination Situation #3

Why did you procrastinate and what happened?

What do you wish you'd done instead?

Reflection Questions

1. Do you notice any similarities among your three procrastination memories?

2. What can you do to reduce procrastination in the future?

#6 Visualization

When you're struggling to find the motivation to finish an assignment you don't like, visualization helps. Try picturing yourself finished with your work. How would it feel to know it's done? What fun thing would you do after you're done? How would it feel to do that fun thing guilt-free knowing you already finished your work?

In the space below, draw a picture of yourself that represents your answers to the above questions.

Briefly describe your picture:

#7 Maximizing Breaks

We can't work ALL the time. Sometimes we need a break. Either we finished a big task and need a reward, or we're struggling to come up with an idea and need to step away from the work for a while. Did you know that "step away" time can be helpful to your creativity? It's true! Ever wonder why your best ideas come to you in the shower? Sometimes we need to step away from a creative task for a moment in order for a good idea to strike.

When you need some "step away" time from an assignment that has you stumped, what are 5, 15-minute things you could do?These could be things that are fun, productive, or a combination of both.

1.

2.

3.

4.

5.

When you want to reward yourself for a job well done before beginning your next homework assignment, what are 5 15-minute things you could do?

1.

2.

3.

4.

5.

#8 Parkinson's Law

Parkinson's Law states that work expands to fill the time we give it. That means that if you give yourself a week to finish a homework assignment, it will probably take the whole week, but if you give yourself one night, you'll probably finish it in a night. That's because work expands like a balloon to fill the time we give it. There are two reasons this happens: Time Killers, and the Myth of Perfection.

1. Time Killers

The balloon below has a homework task inside. Fill in the rest of the balloon with Time Killers that might distract you and make your work take longer.

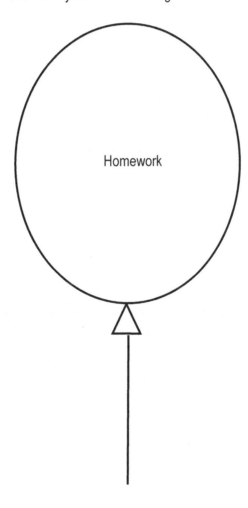

2. Perfection

When we give ourselves too much time to finish an assignment, perfectionists will often continue to look for ways to improve it, even after all criteria are met.

1. Do you consider yourself a perfectionist? Why or why not?

2. What is the difference between "perfect" and "accurate?"

3. When you're revising your work, how do you know if it's "good enough" and time to move on?

4. Parkinson's Law describes how our work takes as long as we give ourselves to finish it. How can you use Parkinson's Law to your advantage?

#9 Worst Case Scenario

Sometimes waiting until the last minute works out fine, but other times it can go drastically wrong. Think of some last minute, unexpected problems that might come up if you wait until the last minute.

Brainstorm a few of them below:

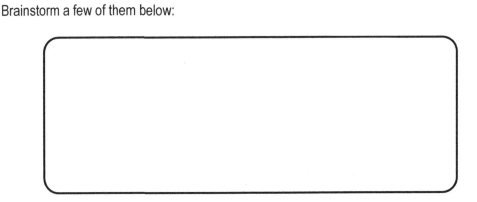

Look at some of the worst-case scenarios you thought of. Pick your favorite(s) and use it to finish the rest of this story. Feel free to be silly! Remember, the point of this exercise is to help you remember the problems that can occur if you procrastinate, and it's easier to remember things if they are funny.

It was 8:00pm on Monday night. My paper was due at midnight. I'd known about it for 3 weeks, but kept procrastinating until now. "I'll be OK," I thought to myself. "I'm a pretty fast writer, especially when I'm up against a deadline. I have 4, uninterrupted hours to write." I sat down to begin my work, when suddenly….

#10 Device Checking

One of the biggest Time Killers is checking our electronic devices. Did someone contact me? Did I miss something funny? Logic would suggest that if we check our phone and don't see anything interesting, we'd stop checking it, but the exact opposite is true. It's like gambling. The more you lose, the more you want to play because maybe next time you'll get lucky. The same is true for device checking. "Nobody wants to get a hold me…but maybe they do… now?"

Are you a device checker? Why? Circle the degree to which each question applies to you

1. I am afraid my friends are having fun without me

| 1 | 2 | 3 | 4 | 5 | 6 | 7 | 8 | 9 | 10 |
| Disagree | | | | | | | | | Agree |

2. I am bored and it fills the time

| 1 | 2 | 3 | 4 | 5 | 6 | 7 | 8 | 9 | 10 |
| Disagree | | | | | | | | | Agree |

3. I am afraid I'll miss out on an important opportunity

| 1 | 2 | 3 | 4 | 5 | 6 | 7 | 8 | 9 | 10 |
| Disagree | | | | | | | | | Agree |

4. It's a habit that I can't break

| 1 | 2 | 3 | 4 | 5 | 6 | 7 | 8 | 9 | 10 |
| Disagree | | | | | | | | | Agree |

Reflection Questions

1. For which statement did you circle the highest number?

2. What can you do to address that concern?

3. Which electronic device in your life is the most distracting?

4. Why?

5. Still having difficulty putting your device down? Try unplugging! Go a few hours with absolutely no access to technology. Do you think you could do it? What would you do instead?

PART 3
LET'S GET MOTIVATED

Let's say you took a painting class. You learned how to mix colors, use a brush, apply shading, and a ton of other painting skills. Then you go to make your first masterpiece and realize you don't have a canvas. You won't get very far because all of those painting skills you learned don't matter until you have a canvas. Motivation is the canvas of time management skills. You may have all of the time management resources and strategies in the world, but unless you have the motivation to apply them, they are relatively useless.

The problem with motivation, however, is that it can be difficult to come by. A variety of factors including stress, health, family, friends, environment, boredom, and other distractions can quickly make you unmotivated to work hard in school. In this section, you'll learn how to identify the most stressful points of your year, recognize excuses you tell yourself, combat stress, maintain a healthy lifestyle, and more. There may be times in this section where you'll feel that you're reading a book about health instead of time management. Remember, all the aspects of your life are interrelated and contribute to your performance in school.

When you're stressed out, what do you usually want to eat? If you're anything like me, you probably want to binge on sweets, junk food or other desserts. We react the same way with time management. When we get stressed at school, we tend to want to overindulge in the "Desserts" or fun things in our Time Diet, and leave the difficult Meat tasks and frustrating Vegetable tasks for later. The more stressed and frustrated we are the more difficult our Meats and Vegetables become and being productive is next to impossible.

The most important part of this section is the final worksheet, your action plan. This will help you turn all of the information you learned into a concrete plan you can apply in your studies. With a little practice, you'll be able to maintain a balanced Time Diet, even in times of stress or frustration. Good luck!

#1 Excuses

When we procrastinate, don't meet a deadline, or don't do as well as we'd like in a class, we tend to make excuses. It's easier to see those excuses in other people than it is in ourselves. Think about the excuses you've heard your friends make and list them below.

1. The Excuse:

    Why is it an excuse?

    What would you tell this friend?

2. The Excuse:

    Why is it an excuse?

    What would you tell this friend?

3.   The Excuse:

          Why is it an excuse?

          What would you tell this friend?

4.   The Excuse:

          Why is it an excuse?

          What would you tell this friend?

Have you ever made any of these excuses before? Did you realize you were making an excuse at the time?

#2 Staying Healthy

When you're in the middle of studying for finals, finding time to eat right and exercise is probably the last thing on your mind, but staying healthy is important to maintaining a low stress level. That's why it's important to have a "stay healthy plan" at the beginning of the semester. Consider the factors that make eating healthy and exercising difficult, and how you'll counter balance those difficulties.

1. Healthy Eating

Difficulties   **Solutions**

2. Exercising

Difficulties   **Solutions**

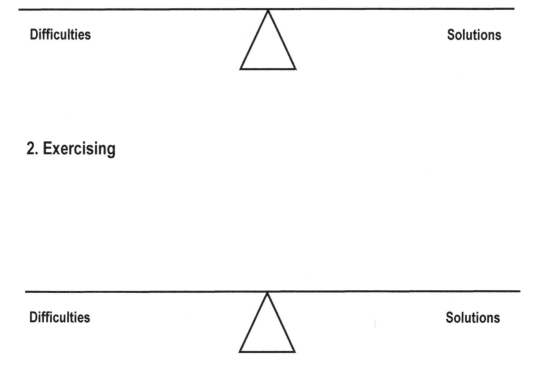

#3 Anticipate Your Struggles

Stress has a way of sneaking up on you during the school year, but if you think of your stress triggers in advance, they don't have to catch you by surprise. Think of the situations that stress you out the most, and when during the school year they are most likely to happen. This will help you anticipate your struggles so you can adjust your schedule accordingly.

Academics stress me out when.....

This is most likely to happen....(what part of the year?)

Friends stress me out when...

This is most likely to happen...

Family stresses me out when...

This is most likely to happen...

#4 Slow Day List

When you're super busy, you might catch yourself saying, *"Why didn't I start this earlier??"* You might promise yourself that the next time you have a free weekend, you're going to start working ahead so you don't end up in this situation again. But then...you forget.

That's why a "Slow Day List" is so important.

When you catch yourself doing something that you could have done earlier, pull out your Slow Day List and write it down. Then, when you have a slow weekend without a lot of school work, you can pull out the Slow Day List and remind yourself of a few ways you can use that free time to get ahead!

For the next week, keep a Slow Day List. Keep track of things that you could have done earlier in the semester.

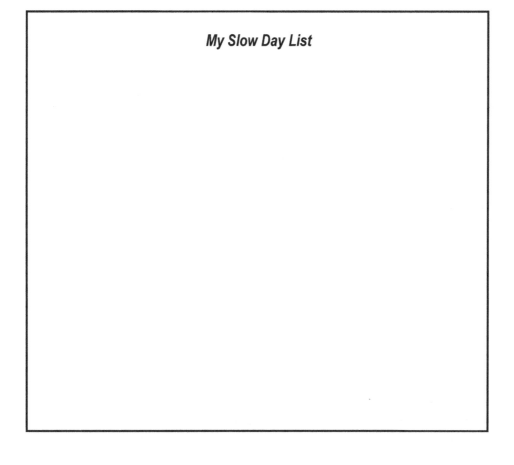

My Slow Day List

Reflection Questions

1. Look at the items on your Slow Day List. Why do you think you put these tasks off until later?

2. What do you think of the concept of a Slow Day List? Do you think it will work for you?

3. Where will you keep your Slow Day List so it's easily accessible?

#5 How to Say No

Sometimes students feel stressed because they overcommit to things in their schedules. It's tempting to sign up for a million extracurricular activities, in addition to honors classes, and family and friend responsibilities. Knowing how and when to say "No" is important.

Think about a time you were asked to join a club, or wanted to commit to another activity:

What was the activity or commitment you considered?

When you're faced with a new time commitment, instead of asking "Do I *want* to do this?" you need to ask yourself a few different questions. For the activity listed above, answer the following questions:

1. Do I have time for this activity?

2. Will it help out a friend?

3. Will it add to my resume?

4. Does it support my skills, goals, or passions?

Now take a look at your answers to the questions above. If you answered "no" to all of the questions, why are you doing the activity? You only have 24 hours in the day and you need to use them wisely. Use the space below to brainstorm a few reasons that people overcommit themselves:

Why do People Overcommit?

#6 Creating Action Items

Do you ever spend time worrying? We all do occasionally, but it adds to your stress and wastes your time and energy. Here is a way to help.

In the space below, write down ALL of your worries at the moment.

My Worries

Worries are just thoughts in your head unless we do something about them. An Action Item is a task you can add to your To-Do list to address a worry. For example, if your worry is "failing a test" the action item is "studying." Look at your worry list above and try to think of "Action Items" for as many of them as you can.

Worries	Action Item

Reflection Questions

1. For which worries were you unable to think of Action Items?

2. If you can't do anything about a worry, then there is no use in worrying about it because it's out of your control. Easier said than done! What are some strategies you can use to help you worry less about things you can't control?

3. Sometimes it's hard to see when you're wasting your time worrying, but it's easier to see when a friend does it. Have you watched a friend worry needlessly lately? What was the situation, and what did you say to him or her?

#7 Write a Letter to the Future

Stress is a real problem in school, but it's helpful to remember that half the stress of getting it all done comes from *worrying about* getting it all done. For example, if we used some of the energy we spent worrying about a math test to study for the math test, we'd be much more productive and less stressed, but that's difficult to do when you're in the middle of a tense, stressful time.

Now that you're calm, use the space below to write a letter to yourself in the future, when you're stressed about your school work. What do you want your future self to remember? What would you say to calm yourself down? Which class do you think you'll be stressed about? Save this letter and pull it out when you need it.

Dear Self,

**Love,
Me**

#8 Ask For Help

Don't forget that smart, successful students ask for help when they need it! Don't be afraid of looking stupid, or asking a dumb question. Your teachers are there to help you succeed.

Sometimes, students don't know *how* to ask for help. Fill out the following information about asking for help so it will be easy to do when you need it:

1. What is your most difficult subject/class?

2. What is your teacher's name?

3. When is he/she available to answer questions?

4. Where is he/she available to answer questions?

5. If you've never asked for help in a class before, why not?

6. Pretend you are a teacher and a student came and asked you for your help. What would you think of that student? Would you think he/she was smart? Stupid? Responsible? Irresponsible?

7. If you were a teacher, would you prefer a student came to you for help right before a deadline or in advance? Why?

#9 Goal Sheet

Sometimes when we think we have a *time* management problem, what we really have is a *motivation* management problem. We have the time management strategies we need, but we just aren't motivated to apply them. When this happens to you, it's important to reconnect with your "why." Why are you working so hard? What are your goals? When you know the "why," the "how" becomes that much easier.

When it comes to goals, keeping them close and visible is important. Think of three things you are working toward this year or this semester. Write them down below, and then either rip out this page or write them on a separate piece of paper and put it somewhere you'll see it frequently.

My Goals

1.

2.

3.

Where will you post these goals?

#10 Action Plan

Congratulations! You've made it to the end of this workbook, but your time management journey is just beginning. You've learned a lot of information, now it's time to synthesize and apply it.

In Part 1 you learned about being organized. We talked about the importance of having both a daily list and a calendar. You categorized your tasks into Meat, Vegetable, and Dessert food groups, and learned how to break up a study schedule into manageable chunks.

Part 2 was all about focus. You identified the time of day you're most focused and productive, and which Time Killers are most likely to distract you.

In Part 3, you reflected on your motivation. Stress is a huge motivation killer and you explored some ways to combat stress so you're motivated to apply the time management skills you're learning.

Now what will you *do* with this information? Identify three actions you will take as a result of this workbook and how it will help you in school.

My Time Management Action Plan

As a result of this workbook, I plan to:

1.

2.

3.

Which will help me in school because:

NOTES

NEXT STEPS

Congratulations! You finished all three sections. You now know how to get organized, remain focused while you work, and stay motivated to keep working. Here are your next steps.

1. Practice, Practice, Practice
The skills you learned in this workbook must become habits before they can become truly useful. For example, you might need to force yourself to use your list and calendar for a month before it becomes routine. Don't be discouraged. You can do it!

2. Talk to Your Friends
Time management isn't exactly the most thrilling topic of conversation, but enlisting the help of your friends can be a great way to stay organized. Ask how they manage their time, what their distractions are, and how the deal with those distractions.

3. Reassess
If you try a few strategies and after a couple weeks or months you still aren't feeling organized, reassess your plan. Maybe you chose a method or strategy that doesn't work with your learning style. Maybe your schedule requires a different plan. It's important to monitor your progress so you know

4. Talk to Your Teachers or Professors
Your teachers are there to help you and you shouldn't be afraid to ask for help. Tell them that you recognize the importance of time management and it's something you're working on.

5. Bring Emily to Your School
I would love to come speak to your school, class, or program. Email Emily@TheTimeDiet.org for booking inquiries.

MORE FROM EMILY SCHWARTZ

Emily is a speaker and trainer based in Phoenix, AZ and is available to come speak nationwide to your school. Speaking offerings include both student events and professional development for instructors. For more info, please email **Emily@TheTimeDiet.org** or visit **www.TheTimeDiet.org.**

Check out these other titles available on Amazon.com

The Time Diet: Time Management for College Survival - A great resources for current and future college students

The Time Diet: Digestible Time Management - An application of The Time Diet method for busy adults.

How to Speak so People Will Buy: Public Speaking Skills to Build Your Business - Public speaking skills will improve all aspects of your job and this book shows you how.

Life in Cut Time: Time Management for Music Teachers - A practical guide specifically for K-12 and University music professionals.

All titles available on Amazon.com. For bulk orders, please email The Time Diet LLC at Emily@TheTimeDiet.org